This Book Belongs To...

Name:

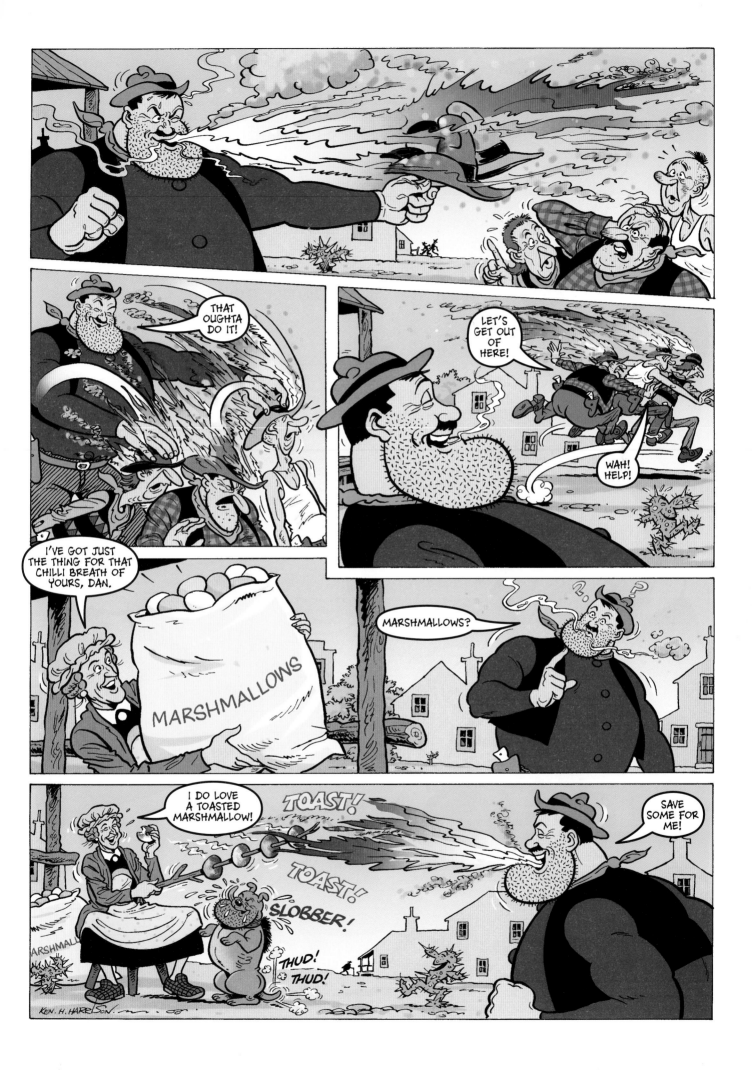

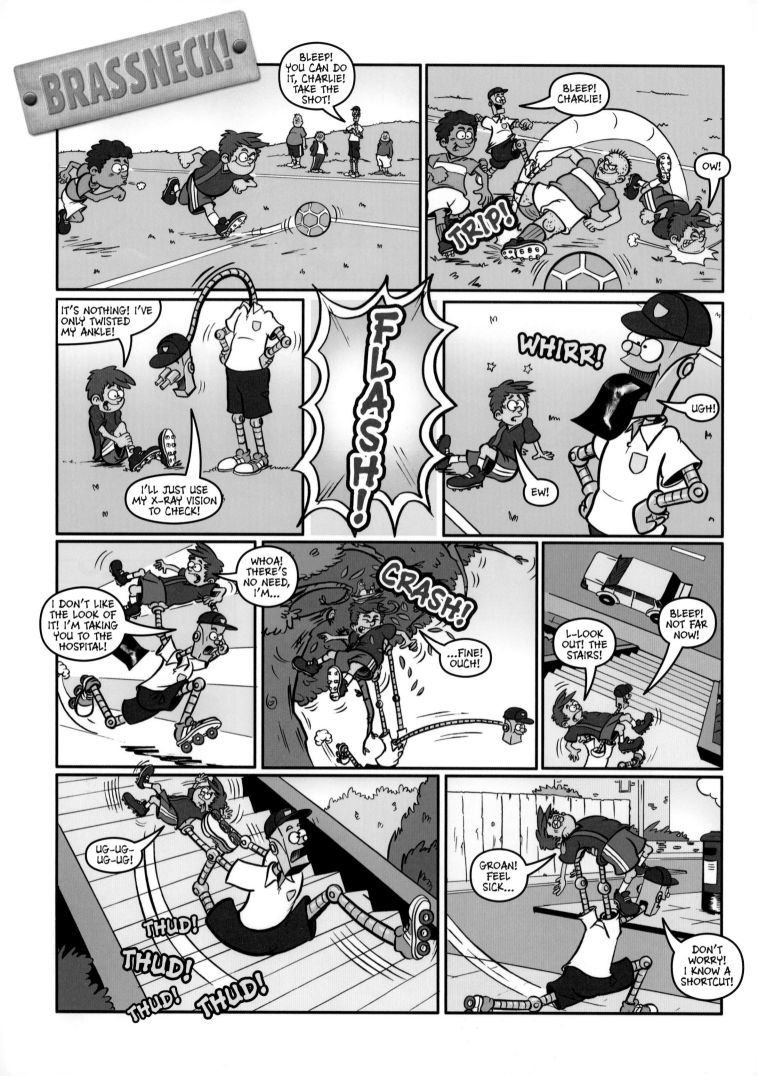

OKAY, CLOTT! TARGET PRACTICE! SEE IF YOU CAN HIT THIS TARGET!

YES, HEADMASTER!

SO...

KA-BOOM!

ARRRGH!!!

SUFFERING SERGEANTS AND JIBBERING GENERALS! WHAT WAS THAT?

URRGH! I WAS SO CLOSE!

GIVE ME THAT THING! THIS IS A RIFLE RANGE! NOT A BAZOOKA RANGE!

WHEN CAN I HAVE THAT BACK? MY NAN GAVE IT TO ME!

SNATCH!

YOU CAN HAVE IT BACK ON THE 33RD OF NOTTEMBER!

THANKS!

OKAY, YOU BROKE IT, YOU FIX IT. FILL UP THAT HOLE WITH SANDBAGS FROM THE STORE.

SANDBAGS

I PROMISE TO DO MY BEST, MR PRESIDENT!

A DAY IN THE LIFE OF A JOCK

Got up this morning...

...and walked the dog!

Had eggs for breakfast...

...and added to my stamp collection during morning break!

Got a wee bit tied up at lunch time!

But after school, caught up with an old acquaintance in the park.

He very kindly offered to help me feed the birds.

Got a life home.

I decided to go to bed early...

...as I needed my beauty sleep!

A DAY IN THE LIFE OF A GEORDIE

Got up this morning...

...and finished some homework.

Bumped into someone I knew on the way to school.

Agreed to meet up later and shook on it!

Played rock, paper, scissors during break (I won).

Tried haggis for lunch (I didn't like it much).

Stopped off at the zoo after school to feed the fish.

Then did some star-gazing before going home...

...Will sleep well tonight!

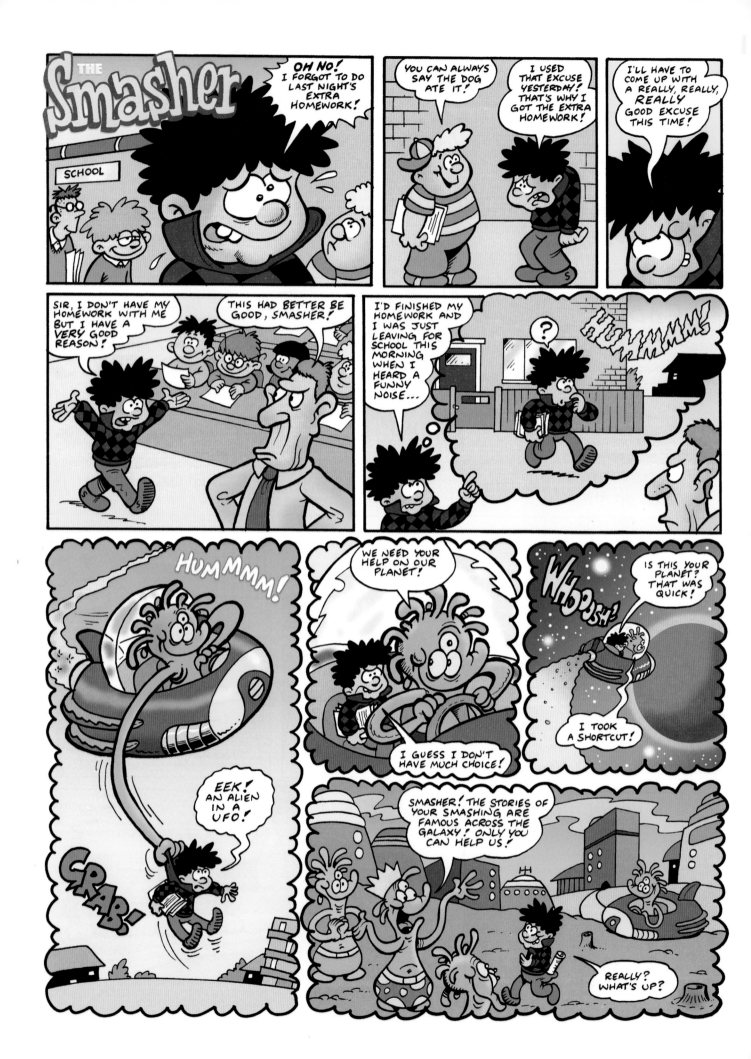

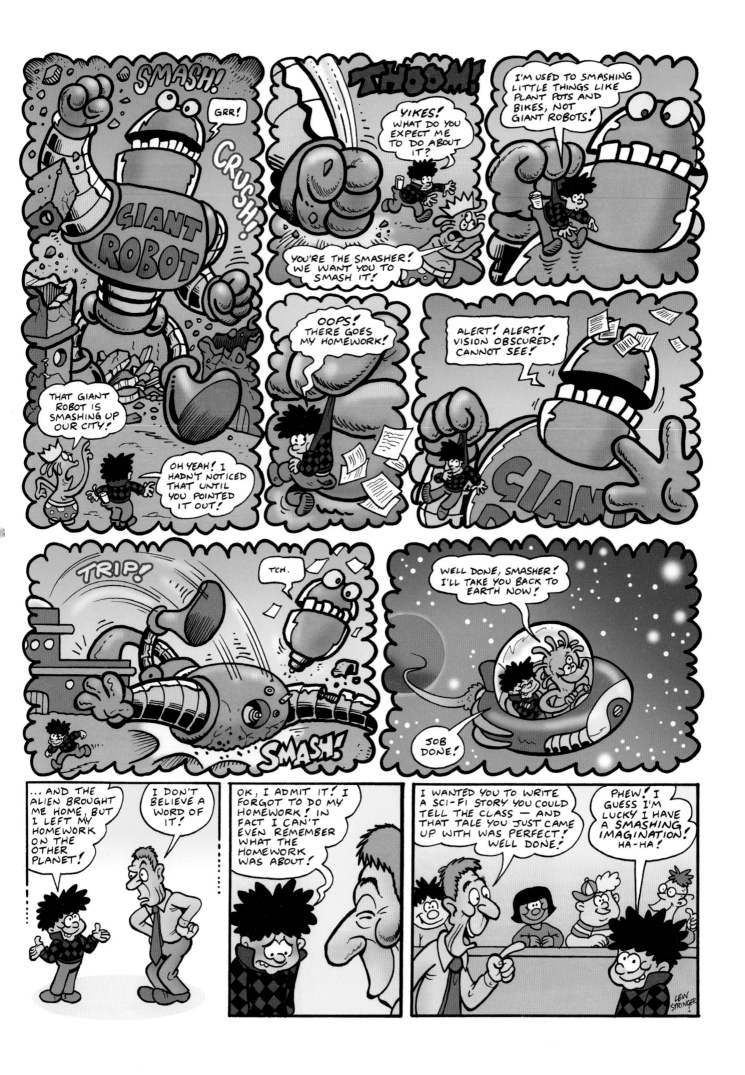

BULLY BEEF and CHIPS

BOB SPED ROUND BEHIND THE PANICKING SHEEP...

...AND JUST IN TIME, TOO! THEY HAD RUN RIGHT TO THE EDGE OF A SHEER CLIFF!

ONE LAMB, WHO HAD LOST TOUCH WITH ITS MOTHER, RAN HEADLONG OVER THE EDGE.

THE POOR CREATURE STUMBLED AND FELL DOWN THE STEEP SLOPE.

MEH!

AT THE BOTTOM LAY A RIVER, FULL OF POWERFUL CURRENTS AT THIS TIME OF YEAR.

THE CURRENT'S GOT HIM, BOB! WE MUST ACT QUICKLY!

BOB KNEW EXACTLY WHAT HE HAD TO DO.

THE BRAVE DOG PLUNGED DOWN THE CLIFF FACE...

HE'S BEING SWEPT AWAY, BOB! QUICKLY NOW!

BOB LEAPT INTO THE FREEZING WATER, THINKING ONLY TO SAVE THE LAMB FROM DROWNING.

BOB WAS A POWERFUL SWIMMER AND HE SOON HAD THE LAMB BACK ON DRY LAND.

WELL DONE, BOB! THAT LAMB WAS A GONER FOR SURE, IF IT WASN'T FOR YOU!

THAT'S IT... LET THE LAMB BACK TO ITS MOTHER NOW.

IT'S FROZEN THROUGH. WE'D BEST GET THIS ONE UNDER SOME HEAT LAMPS TO DRY IT OUT.

WITH THE LAMB RETURNED TO SAFETY, THEY BROUGHT THE HERD IN WITH NO MORE INCIDENT.

THAT'S US FOR THE NIGHT, BUT I WONDER WHAT SPOOKED THE HERD SO BADLY, BOB?

MORE BLACK BOB LATER!

ANOTHER DAY, ANOTHER CHANCE TO GO OUT AND DO SOME SNOOPING THROUGH KEYHOLES!

YOU'RE NOT GOING OUT TODAY, KATE! IT'S FREEZING OUT THERE!

ICY BLAST

BRRR!

COLD WIND

AW, MUM! CAN'T I GO OUT AND DO A LITTLE BIT OF SNOOPING? IT'S SO COOL!

IT'S NOT COOL! FIND A NEW HOBBY! READ A BOOK OR SOMETHING!

THIS IS NO GOOD! THERE ARE NO KEYHOLES IN IT!

SIGH! THE GIRL'S OBSESSED!

ALRIGHT, YOU CAN GO OUT FOR A LITTLE WHILE IF YOU WRAP UP WARM, BUT DON'T SNOOP THROUGH KEYHOLES!

AW, MUM. I PROMISE...

...I PROMISE I'LL ONLY SNOOP FOR A FEW MINUTES! HA-HA!

BAH! THAT'S THE BEST I COULD HOPE FOR I SUPPOSE!

THAT KEYHOLE LOOKS PERFECT FOR SNOOPING THROUGH!

LATER...

KATE'S BEEN OUT FOR AGES! I'D BETTER SEE WHERE SHE IS!

KATE! THERE YOU ARE! YOU PROMISED YOU WOULDN'T BE LONG!

I CAN'T MOVE, MUM! MY NOSE IS F-F-FROZEN TO THE K-K-KEYHOLE!

HA! KEYHOLE SNOOPING WAS A BIT TOO COOL TODAY, EH, KATE?

LEW STRINGER

What I did on my holidays by Winker WATSON

Mr Creep's eyebrows were raised so high, they pushed back his mortar board. He was reading Winker Watson's essay, 'What I did on my holidays'...

It was a sorry sight that befell my eyes when I sauntered into the drawing room shortly after arriving home for Christmas. My sister, Cressida, was draped over the couch like an Autumn leaf on a soggy afternoon.

'What's up, Cressie?' I asked cheeringly, but she barely lifted her head in response.

'Brother,' she croaked, and held out her arms, 'hugs!'

After we hugged I asked her again what was the matter. Soon, the matter came oozing out as if from an open sore. Between sobs, Cressie managed to explain.

'Pinky was coming for Christmas dinner, but now Father says he can't, and that Pinky's a dimwit, and that I mustn't see him any more!'

Which was followed by a great wail of despair.

I guessed that 'Pinky' must be Cressie's latest boyfriend. Now, he may well be a dimwit, but if he's Cressie's favourite dimwit then he's alright by me. So I 'there there'd a bit and then retired to my room to think.

The next morning was Christmas Eve, and I arose early and took a wheelbarrow for a little walk down the garden. I stood by the old chestnut tree til the turkey man came down the road in his truck. I flagged him down and managed to persuade him to let me take the turkey he was delivering to the Watson household in my wheelbarrow.

As soon as he was out of sight, I dumped the turkey in a hedge and ran to the nearest telephone and called Pinky.

At home, Mother picked up the phone. 'Mrs Watson? It's Crabtree, the turkey dealer. I'm terribly sorry but I double-booked – I don't have a turkey for you this year.'
Pinky, putting on his best Crabtree impression and muffling the handset with a hanky, played the part well.

Mother was devastated, there was no way we'd get another turkey anywhere on Christmas Eve. Christmas was ruined.

On cue, Cressie spoke up, saying what a resourceful and clever chap Pinky was, and how she bet he could find them a turkey.

Later, Pinky and I found the turkey just fine. Right where I'd left it. The idea was for Pinky to stroll up to the front door with the bird under his arm, but there was a snag. Wally, my pesky little brother, was running about with a chum playing cowboys, between us and the drive. We'd never get the bird past him unseen, and if he spotted us, he'd spill the beans for sure.

So we nipped round the back and had just clambered in through a window when Father strolled past, in a killing mood on account of the missing turkey. I thought the game was up, but we just had time to hide both turkey and Pinky under the net curtain, me miming leaning on them both like they were an occasional table, and Father fortunately too preoccupied to look too closely.

Now we just had to get Pinky and the bird to the front door so it looked like he was just arriving. Trouble was, Mother was on the phone in the hall, trying to find another turkey. We couldn't hang about, what with Father on the rampage. We had to act fast or we'd be caught red-handed. Never mind the turkey, it was our goose that would be cooked.

Before I'd thought what to do, the door flew open and Wally's pal thundered past, with Wally in hot pursuit. They were like a pair of over-excited puppies with a string of sausages. Luckily they didn't see us, but I saw a chance to solve our little problem. Risky, but we had to try it. With a yank on a nearby rug, I brought down a vase with a mighty crash, which brought Mother off the phone and yelling blue murder after Wally. We'd hidden ourselves and the turkey behind the door, and happily Mother gave chase after Wally and pal, allowing us at last to safely nip along the hall to the front door.

Shortly, the doorbell rang and there was Pinky, playing the knight-in-shining-armour card for all he was worth, turkey under his arm and beaming grin on his chops. The hero of the hour, the man who'd saved Christmas! Even Father had to admit that Pinky might not be such a dimwit after all, and he could hardly now begrudge him joining us for a very jolly Christmas dinner!

Mr Creep lifted his head, and his jaw slowly followed.

'Well, Watson,' he said slowly, 'it's an outrageous tale, but I shall assume it is a work of imaginative fiction... and as such I can't fault it on spelling, grammar, punctuation, use of metaphor and simile, and general style, for a boy of your age.

Later, the boys crowded round Watson. They could tell from the gleam in his eye that there was more to this than the essay revealed.

'I got Cressie's boyfriend the credit for the turkey, so in return I get the credit for Cressie writing my essay for me!', smirked the wangler.

BULLY BEEF and CHIPS

I HAVE TO MAKE SURE THIS CAKE IS DELIVERED IN ONE PIECE.

TITTER! I'LL GIVE HIM A HAND - OR A FOOT!

WATCH YOUR **STEP**, CHIPS. OOPS - TOO LATE!

OOOF!

HERE, LET ME CARRY IT FOR YOU.

CAREFUL WITH THAT CAKE!

IN FACT, I'LL **LIGHTEN THE LOAD** - BY EATING IT MYSELF! HAR-HAR!

GO AHEAD, OPEN IT!

WH-WHAT'S THIS??

I MADE IT FOR YOU. I WAS HOPING WE COULD PUT ALL THIS FIGHTING BEHIND US.

LET'S BE FRIENDS

HERE, CUT YOURSELF THE FIRST SLICE!

THAT'S THE NICEST THING ANYONE'S EVER DONE FOR ME!

GUUUH!

BOP!

HA! WHAT A DOUGHNUT!

KORKY the CAT

CORPORAL CLOTT

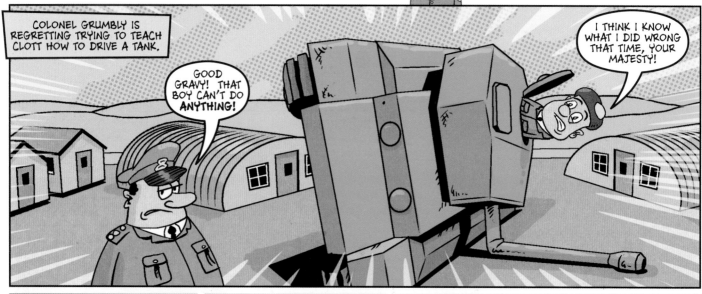

COLONEL GRUMBLY IS REGRETTING TRYING TO TEACH CLOTT HOW TO DRIVE A TANK.

GOOD GRAVY! THAT BOY CAN'T DO **ANYTHING!**

I THINK I KNOW WHAT I DID WRONG THAT TIME, YOUR MAJESTY!

STOP CALLING ME YOUR MAJESTY! I'M NOT **THE** QUEEN!

OH, BUT WAIT! THAT GIVES ME AN IDEA! HA-HA-HA!

HA-HA-HA! WHY ARE WE LAUGHING?

BUCKINGHAM PALACE...

OKAY, IT'S YOUR JOB TO DO NOTHING! NOTHING, CLOTT! CAN YOU DO THAT? STAND STILL?

NOTHING BUT GUARD THE QUEEN. GOT IT!

NO! **NO GUARDING!** THAT POLICE MAN WITH THE MACHINE GUN IS THE REAL GUARD! YOU'RE JUST HERE FOR THE TOURISTS! STAND STILL! DO NOTHING!!!

AYE, AYE, CAPTAIN!

JUST REMEMBER! STILL AS A STATUE!

AND I'M NOT A CAPTAIN, I'M A COLONEL!

YES, CHIEF!

EIGHT HOURS LATER...

HAD A GOOD DAY, CLOTT? MANAGED TO STAY STILL ALL DAY?

YES, YOUR LORDSHIP!

REALLY? ODD THAT THERE'S SOMEONE WHO LOOKS A LOT LIKE YOU ALL OVER THE INTERNET!

THIS IS FROM THE WATSON FAMILY'S FACEBOOK WITH THE CAPTION, "FUN AND GAMES AT THE PALACE!"

OH THAT? THAT WAS ONE MOMENTARY SLIP UP, YOUR WORSHIP!

WHAT ABOUT THIS TRENDING ON TWITTER? #CRAZYGUARD

AND WHO'S THAT WEARING YOUR HAT?

I CAN'T REMEMBER HER NAME. SHE WAS REALLY NICE THOUGH.

HERE YOU ARE GIVING OUT FREE PIGGYBACKS!

AND HERE'S A VIDEO OF YOU PUSHING IN LINE AT THE ICE CREAM VAN!

OUT OF THE WAY! THE QUEEN WANTS A MINTY MAGNUM!

BARGE! SHOVE!

IT WASN'T FOR THE QUEEN, WAS IT?

THIS HAT IS VERY, VERY HOT!

COME ON! WE'RE GOING BACK. WHERE'S YOUR RIFLE?

RIFLE?

I HAD A RIFLE, DID I?

NEARBY...

WHERE DID HE GET THAT TOY RIFLE FROM?

ARE YOU SURE IT'S A TOY?

Black Bob

THE LATE WINTER BLIZZARD LEFT THE FARM UNDER A CARPET OF SNOW FOR A WEEK, BUT SOON THE WORST WAS PAST AND THE SNOW MELTED AWAY.

FRESH GRASS IS BETTER FOR THE SHEEP, BOB. WE SHOULD GET THEM BACK INTO THE FIELDS.

HANG ON, THAT'S MY PHONE.

BREEP! BREEP!

HELLO? HI, HENRY. NO, MY SHEEP WERE ALL SAFE INDOORS – AND I HAVEN'T SEEN ANY OF YOURS.

IT WAS ANDREW'S NEIGHBOUR, HENRY WILSON, WONDERING IF HE HAD SEEN SOME SHEEP OF HIS, WHICH HAD GONE MISSING.

OUT ON THE HILLS, ANDREW WAS PUZZLED WHEN HE SAW HIS FENCE WAS BROKEN.

THAT WASN'T LIKE THAT A FEW DAYS AGO. THE SHEEP COULD GET OUT ONTO THE ROAD!

GO STOP THEM, BOB! BRING THEM BACK HERE.

BOB SPED INTO POSITION, TURNING THE SHEEP AWAY FROM THE BREAK IN THE FENCE.

HMM... THE WEATHER DIDN'T BREAK THIS FENCE – IT'S BEEN DELIBERATELY BROKEN!

ANDREW DECIDED TO INSPECT THE REST OF HIS FENCING. SURE ENOUGH, FURTHER AROUND THE HILL...

THIS HAS BEEN DONE ON PURPOSE TOO! WHAT'S GOING ON?

JUST THEN, A POLICE CAR AND A LAND ROVER APPEARED. ANDREW TOLD BOB TO TAKE THE SHEEP TO THE NEXT FIELD WHILE HE INVESTIGATED.

HELLO, WHO'S THIS, THEN?

IT WAS HENRY WILSON AND A POLICEMAN.

ANDREW, HENRY SAYS YOU MAY HAVE SOME OF HIS SHEEP ON YOUR LAND.

DON'T BE DAFT, HENRY. I'VE PLENTY SHEEP OF MY OWN!

MY LADS SAY THEY SAW THEM, GLEN. SHEEP STEALING IS A SERIOUS CRIME, YOU KNOW!

BOB HAD TAKEN THE SHEEP TO THE FIELD, BUT THERE WAS A SURPRISE WAITING FOR HIM! MORE SHEEP - AND BOB COULD TELL THEY WEREN'T ANDREW GLEN'S!

IF THE POLICEMAN SAW THESE SHEEP, THERE WOULD BE TROUBLE!

BOB SET ABOUT ROUNDING UP THE STRANGE SHEEP, TO KEEP THEM AWAY FROM HIS OWNER'S FLOCK.

MEANWHILE...

IF I SEE ANY OF YOUR SHEEP, I'LL BE SURE TO LET YOU KNOW, BUT YOU SHOULD REALLY TAKE BETTER CARE OF THEM!

IN FACT, AREN'T THOSE YOUR SHEEP IN THE ROAD?

BOB HAD SHEPHERDED THE MYSTERY FLOCK THROUGH THE HOLES IN THE FENCE JUST IN TIME.

HENRY WILSON WAS MADE TO LOOK A FOOL IN FRONT OF ANDREW GLEN AND THE ANNOYED POLICEMAN!

HO-HO!

GET THOSE SHEEP OFF THE ROAD, MR WILSON! YOU'RE CAUSING A NUISANCE!

BUT... HOW DID THIS HAPPEN?

MORE BLACK BOB LATER!

CLUE ONE
The culprit wasn't wearing glasses.

CLUE TWO
An eyewitness said you could definitely see the thief's eyes.

CLUE THREE
Cuddles was having his afternoon tantrum, er, we mean nap, so it wasn't him.

CLUE FOUR
Footprints were found at the scene of the crime, not paw-prints!

SMASHER

KEYHOLE KATE

GREEDY PIGG

KORKY THE CAT

DESPERATE DAN

CUDDLES

CORPORAL CLOTT

BABY-FACE FINLAYSON

BULLY BEEF

CLUE FIVE
The recipe-nabber was spotted wearing a hat.

CLUE SIX
The culprit wasn't related to Aunt Aggie!

CLUE SEVEN
Whoever did it wasn't visiting from Beanotown.

CLUE EIGHT
Moustache clippings were found where the recipe was taken. Ugh!

Answer: Greedy Pigg

BIG HEAD AND THICK HEAD

Black Bob

ANDREW GLEN WAS REPAIRING A DAMAGED FENCE ON HIS LAND.

THIS WAS DEFINITELY DONE DELIBERATELY, BOB.

SHEEP HAVE PASSED THROUGH HERE.

AND THIS DYE IS THE COLOUR OF HENRY WILSON'S SHEEP MARKINGS.

JUST THEN, ANDREW HAD A VISIT FROM A NEIGHBOUR...

JUST COME TO SAY GOODBYE, ANDREW. I'M SELLING UP. WILSON OFFERED ME A GOOD PRICE FOR MY FARM.

I'M SORRY TO HEAR THAT, JOHN. YOU'VE BEEN A GOOD NEIGHBOUR.

ODD THAT WILSON DIDN'T MENTION BUYING THE ABNETT FARM WHEN HE WAS HERE.

I KNOW HE WANTS TO EXPAND. I THOUGHT HE'D HAVE MENTIONED IT.

BACK AT THE FARM...

THE CATTLE ARE GONE! AND I KNOW I DIDN'T LEAVE THIS GATE OPEN.

GO FIND THEM, LAD.

BOB SOON FOUND THE MISSING HERD.

WHERE DO YOU LOT THINK YOU'RE GOING?

SURE ENOUGH, THEY SOON CAUGHT AND HEADED OFF THE HERD.

I THINK WE'VE EARNED OUR LUNCH TODAY, BOB.

SITTING AT LUNCH, ANDREW HEARD A NOISE FROM THE BARN.

SOMETHING'S WRONG, BOB.

THE BARN WAS ON FIRE!

WE'VE STILL GOT LAMBS IN THERE!

THE BRAVE DOG LEAPED INTO THE SHEEP PEN.

MOMENTS LATER HE RETURNED, LAMB SAFELY GRIPPED IN HIS JAWS.

HE PUSHED THE BOLT HOLDING THE PEN CLOSED TO THE SIDE...

...LETTING THE SHEEP ESCAPE, BEFORE THINKING OF LEAVING HIMSELF.

BEFORE HE COULD GET OUT, A BURNING BALE OF HAY TOPPLED BESIDE BOB.

YOU'RE HURT, LAD. WE NEED TO GET THE VET FOR YOU.

LATER...

SORRY, ANDREW, WE NEED TO TALK TO YOU AGAIN. IT'S ABOUT BOB THIS TIME.

YOUR DOG ATTACKED MY SHEEP!

RUBBISH.

I FILMED THIS ON MY PHONE NOT AN HOUR AGO.

BUT BOB HAD BEEN AT THE VET'S HAVING HIS PAW BANDAGED.

HE COULDN'T HAVE BEEN CHASING SHEEP!

SO IT WASN'T BOB YOU SAW.

THAT MEANS THERE'S STILL A VICIOUS DOG OUT THERE.

WELL, PERHAPS IT WILL HAVE GONE AWAY NOW.

I THINK WE SHOULD HAVE A LOOK AROUND YOUR PLACE, MR WILSON.

DESPITE WILSON'S PROTESTS, THEY SOON FOUND AN AGGRESSIVE SHEEPDOG THAT LOOKED VERY LIKE BOB!

BOB WAS IN THE CLEAR, BUT HENRY WILSON WASN'T!

ALL THAT FUSS BECAUSE WILSON WANTED TO DRIVE ME OFF MY FARM, SO HE COULD BUY IT CHEAP!

HE'D NO CHANCE AGAINST US, BOB!

THE END!

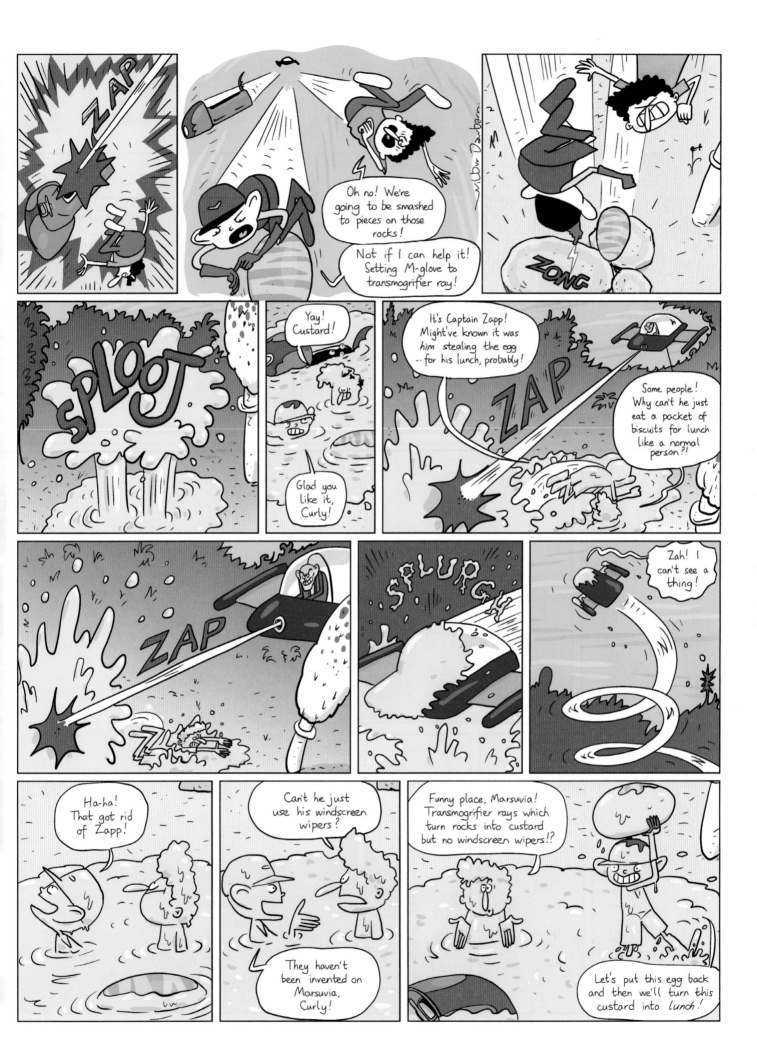

CORPORAL CLOTT

BIG HEAD AND THICK HEAD ARE DOG SITTING FOR BIG HEAD'S NEIGHBOUR...

SCAMP WILL BE FINE. HE JUST CHASES THE CAT IF NO-ONE'S IN. I'LL BE BACK IN AN HOUR.

THE BOYS DECIDE TO WATCH TV...

JAB! JAB!

I CAN'T GET IT TO TURN ON!

YOU LUMBERING IDIOT! THERE'LL BE SOME SORT OF SWITCH ON THE TV. I'LL FIND IT. HOW DID A LITTLE OLD LADY LIKE THAT GET SUCH A BIG...

...TV?!

KRASH!

OOF!

ARE WE GETTING PAID ENOUGH MONEY DOING THIS TO BUY A NEW TV?

FORGET THE TV!!!

LOOK WHAT YOU DID TO THE CAT!

SUDDENLY, SCAMP MAKES AN APPEARANCE...

ARRGH!

THE DOG!

GRAB!

THE BOYS SPEND AN HOUR GETTING FIT...

THIS COULD NOT GET ANY WORSE!

THIS IS FUN!

COME BACK HERE!

DASH!

THEN IT GETS WORSE...

YOO-HOO! I'M BACK WITH MY SON, LOCAL CAGE FIGHTING HERO "BREAKER" JOHNSON!

YOU'VE BROUGHT ME ONE OF MY SLIPPERS, SCAMP. GOOD BOY!

IT'S A SLIPPER! PHEW! WE'RE IN THE CLEAR!

WHAT HAVE YOU DONE TO MY MUM'S TV?!

YOU KNOW, I COMPLETELY FORGOT ABOUT THE TV!

GET BACK HERE!

MUMMY!

DANDY TOWN 30 MILES

CORPORAL CLOTT

COLONEL GRUMBLY HAS FOUND A WAY TO GET RID OF CLOTT FOR A COUPLE OF DAYS...

CLOTT, I'M PUTTING YOU IN CHARGE OF A DISUSED UNDERGROUND TOP SECRET BASE!

COOL!

DISUSED?

YES, DURING THE SIXTIES THIS PLACE WAS SO TOP SECRET NO-ONE TOLD ANYONE IT WAS HERE, SO NO-ONE KNEW IT EXISTED AND NO-ONE CAME!

THE ARMY ONLY DISCOVERED IT WHEN WE DECIDED TO BUILD A BASE HERE AND FOUND WE ALREADY HAD ONE!

SECRET UNDERGROUND BASE

DON'T TELL ANYONE!

YOUR VITAL MISSION IS TO SWEEP UP AND DUST BEFORE ACTUAL SOLDIERS COME HERE!

AYE, AYE, CAPTAIN!

HERE'S YOUR WEAPON!

THRUST!

GRUMBLY GOES HOME WHILE CLOTT GETS TO WORK...

WAY OUT

TAKE THAT, DUST!

TWO MINUTES LATER...

KITCHEN

WAR ROOM

POW! POW! TAKE THAT, SPACE ALIENS!

CLOTT DECIDES TO EXPLORE...

URRGH! THIS MILK THAT'S BEEN LEFT OUT FOR MORE THAN 50 YEARS HAS GONE OFF!

SNIFF!

SIP!

BULLY BEEF and CHIPS

OH, A LIFE ON THE OCEAN WAVES – WHAT FUN!

NICE HAT, DORK.

ARE YOU COMMANDING A NAVAL VESSEL TOO, BEEFY?

MY BOAT!

YEAH, I'M COMMANDING IT TO DESTROY YOURS.

CRASH!!

AND IT HAS GUN TURRETS FOR TAKING OUT ENEMY SHIPS – OR CHIPS!

SPLAT-AT-AT-AT!

YOU'RE MAKING ME SEE RED, BEEFY!

IT'S TIME TO SUMMON THE AIR FORCE.

SCHROOM!

VROOM!

AAARGH! MY 'DO!

OR SHOULD THAT BE HAIR FORCE?

HA-HA! LOOK AT BULLY BEEF!

YOU MEAN BALDY BEEF!

WANT TO BORROW MY HAT, BEEFY?

CRINGE!

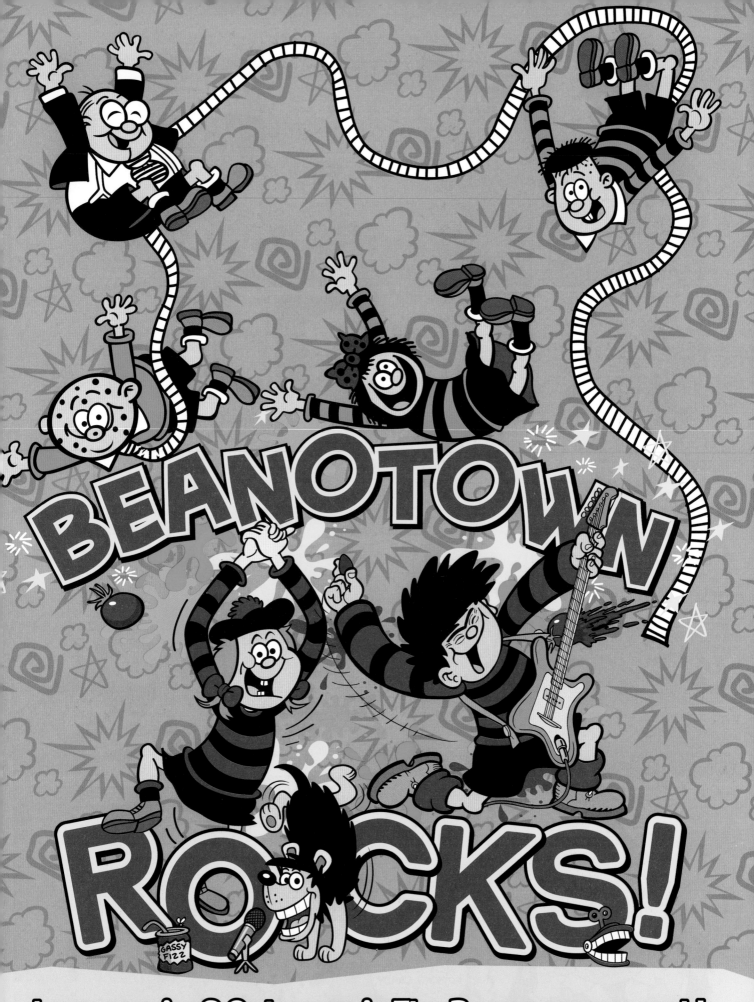